GW00390946

Classic Soul

For SSA Choir With Piano Accompaniment

Arranged by Berty Rice

Cover design by Miranda Harvey.
Music engraved by Andrew Shiels.
Printed in the United Kingdom.

Novello Publishing Limited
8-9 Frith Street, London W1D 3JB

Knock On Wood

Words & Music by Eddie Floyd & Steve Cropper

I don't wan - na lose this good___ thing

7

It's like thun - der, light - ning,

It's like thun - der, light - ning,

It's like thun - der, light - ning,

The way you love me is fright - 'ning, I'd bet - ter knock on wood,

The way you love me is fright - 'ning, I'd bet - ter knock on wood,

The way you love me is fright - 'ning, I'd bet - ter knock on wood,

hit the piano

15

Midnight Train To Georgia

Words & Music by Jim Weatherly

Dreams don't al - ways __ come true,

Dreams don't al - ways come true,

that dreams __ don't al - ways __ come true, __ uh -

uh - uh, no, uh - uh. ooh, hoo, hoo,

uh - uh, no, uh - uh. ooh, hoo, hoo,

uh. So he turned all his hopes, and he ev - en

When ev-er he takes that ride, __ Guess who's gon-na be right by __ his side. __

When ev-er he takes that ride, Guess who's gon-na be right by __ his side. __

place and time, oh yes he is, And I'll be

Dm⁷/G

I know you will. __

I know you will. __

with him, __ on that mid-night train to Geor-

C   Em⁷   Dm⁷   Dm⁷/G

Leav - in' on that mid - night train to Geor - gia woo, woo!

Leav - in' on that mid - night train to Geor - gia woo, woo!

gia.

Am   Am/G   Am/F♯   D⁷

Live in his world, her world is

Live in his world, her world is

I'd ra - ther live in his world, than live with - out him in mine.

Fmaj⁷   Dm⁹/G   C   G/B

dim.

mf

Son of a Preacher Man

Words & Music by John Hurley & Ronnie Wilkins

45

53

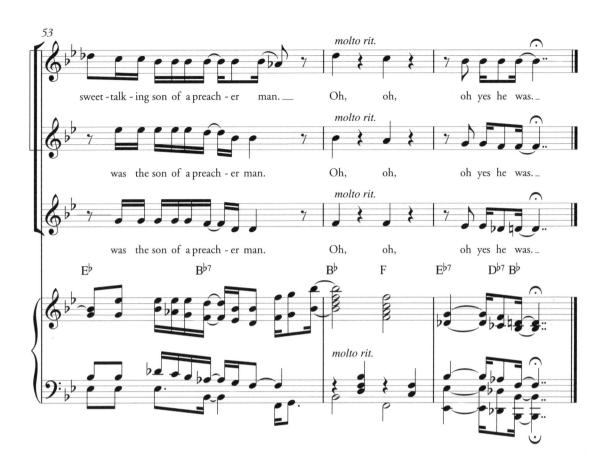

Rescue Me

Words & Music by Carl Smith & Raynard Miner

49

51

lone- ly?— Res-cue me.—

lone- ly?— Res-cue me.—

lone- ly?— Res-cue me.—

Yeah, res - cue me,_____ Yeah, res - cue me,_____

lone - ly, and I'm blue,_____ I need you_____ and your love_ too,_____

Yeah, res - cue me,_____ Yeah, res - cue me,_____

A   D   G

_ res - cue me._____ Take me ba - by

_ come on and res - cue me._____ Come on ba - by,

_ res - cue me._____ Take me ba-

Em⁷   A   D